Proven ways to shift your

PREPARE TO SHIFT

THE WORKBOOK

TERRAND SMITH

To legacy.
Strength, courage, humility, and impact.
Passed from my mother and father. Passed to my daughter,
Yael.
The journey continues.

TABLE OF CONTENTS

Chapter 1
Introduction

It aggravates me when I hear people say, "I want to be an entrepreneur so I can make a lot of money, plan my schedule and be a boss!". Little do they know that entrepreneurship is the exact opposite of this, especially in the early stages. It takes time to get to the level that affords you this type of lifestyle. But the fact is, nobody talks about this.

Also, no one prepares us for the moments when we feel we've given everything we've got, and yet things still don't seem to be moving forward, or going how we want them to go, or at the speed we expect. We participate in pop-up markets, invest in marketing, enroll in startup training programs, and remain in the same phase. We occasionally sell a few units online, possibly dabble in a storefront location and manage to get a few *real customers, aka* non-friends and family, to buy our products or services. But it's never consistent or repetitive. What makes this even worse is that we feel that we don't have the necessary resources to drive or nurture growth, and we have to do it all on our own while juggling 2,800 other responsibilities.

Customers love our product, and we believe it needs to be available to a larger market because more people need what we have. But, our efforts don't seem to get us where we need to go. We feel stuck and can't break through this stage.

It's frustrating and discouraging because this business is not only your hobby or talent; it's your passion. It's your future. One goal is for it to help you achieve financial independence by either being your full-time and sole source of income, a stable secondary income source, or being passed down through family generations. You see, it can improve the quality of life for both yourself, your family, your loved ones and the wider community. How does it feel to have something you know can impact many lives but can't seem to get past step 1? You knew entrepreneurship was work, which you were OK about - but you didn't think it would be like this.

I can relate to all of this. Unfortunately, this is the sentiment of most entrepreneurs I work with across the country. You are part of a club you didn't know existed. It is a familiar feeling for innovators and creators like yourself that have a fantastic product but lack the knowledge, resources, and mentorship needed to grow a profitable, sustainable and scalable business. We bond through the unique challenges faced by high potential, under-resourced, and underfunded small business owners like ourselves.

Here is the bright side. You are a business owner with a fantastic product, and this is not the end of the journey- it's the beginning. Many in our club worked through the common challenges of shifting from hobby to growth and continuing to operate thriving businesses. What we need to break through the hobby stage is often not taught in business school or startup programming- at least not from what I have seen. It's taught through the community. It is taught through sharing best practices and being transparent about what has worked or hasn't. It's about learning from resilient and committed entrepreneurs who have shared similar experiences and understand our unique struggles. We must promote these wins, share the methods, and support others through them.

This is one of the reasons I published this workbook. I have worked with close to 1,000 entrepreneurs across the country with this same profile, and I considered myself one of this profile as well. I didn't plan for entrepreneurship; it *planned* for me. I went to business school, but did not study this. I didn't grow up around successful entrepreneurs that scaled their businesses to the level I aspired. I didn't have a pool of money to tap into or a network of like-minded entrepreneurs or experts to coach me through the early stages. Both my parents were successful in their own right, but both had sadly passed away when I first launched my own business, so they were not able to share the knowledge or provide encouragement.

I needed what was written in this workbook and offered through my company at that time. I wanted to create the support I needed when I launched 37 Oaks - a commerce development and learning laboratory dedicated to entrepreneurs. We educate and prepare them for growth through e-commerce, wholesale, storefronts, and pop-up markets. Although we offer over 30 courses through 37 Oaks University, countless programs and cohorts, a SOKONI e-commerce marketplace, and a community of coaches, resources, and connections, I realized something was missing. We teach the technical side of growing online and in retail, but what about the non-technical and practical skills needed to reach the growth stage? These go hand-in-hand. A foundational shift needs to occur in how we think and work to successfully transform our businesses from a hobby to the growth stage. This is what I wish every entrepreneur knew and did before working with me and what I wish I knew and did before embarking on this journey.

I spent nearly 20 years as a National Buyer for some of the largest retailers in the United States. If you know anything about Buyers, they are responsible for virtually every aspect of getting the product to the customer in a profitable way. This includes responsibilities for assortments, marketing, financials, negotiations, supply chain, market research, store brands, and e-commerce choices. I managed categories ranging from hair accessories to pet care, cough and cold, incontinence, and so on. I have worked with neighborhood and large multinational brands and for stores from 50 to over 10,000 locations. Let's say I have put in my 10,000 hours in the consumer packaged goods (CPG) and retail world to become a master in my field.

When I launched 37 Oaks, I didn't really know what I was doing, what I was selling, who my customers were, and what made me valuable to them. I knew I loved everything

related to retail, commerce, and distribution
I had experience and great credibility fron.
experience. But a reality check was that my credio..
established with retail corporations, not small businesses o.
the organizations supporting them. Selling to this new market
was challenging, and I will discuss that in future chapters. In
addition, I had limited time and funds, and the added pressure
of entrepreneurship being my sole income source. Does this
sound familiar? But what I didn't know yet, was that I was
more than competent and committed to figuring it all out.

I knew there were different stages to entrepreneurship, but
I didn't realize that moving from hobby to growth is one of the
more frustrating ones because this is when we are at our "least"
in this entrepreneurial journey. We are the least experienced,
the least certain, have the least amount of resources, the least
amount of money, and the least amount of knowledge.

Stage 1: Ideation

This is when you identify talent, skill, need, or opportunity,
and it sparks a thought of turning it into a business. There is
not much structure around it now, just an initial concept.

Stage 2: Hobby

This is when you begin incubating the idea. You may say, "I
may have something here." or hear others say, "You should start

business." You have an early stage version of your product, a prototype, and start selling it to customers at your leisure. You aren't focused on formal business management practices but are producing, marketing, and selling products casually. Although there is little talk about financials, marketing, or significant business development efforts.

Stage 3: Startup

The important part about this stage is that you make a deliberate decision to start a business that will grow. You begin to add structure using business management principles because you have chosen to organize and operate a business and will take on greater than normal financial risks. Your operations are immature, and you have ways to go to formalize and structure your business into a well-oiled machine. You are investing, strategizing, and intentionally building a solid foundation for future growth. You begin to collect and use data to define your customer, refine your product and gain clarity.

Stage 4: Growth

Now you have increased confidence by getting through the startup stage. You have a solid business model in place and want to solidify your position in the market, and home in on scaling to new markets. Operations and management get more structured and intense. Your team is growing, and you are investing in technology, systems & services to operate it.

Stage 5: Maturity

You have sustainable sales & profit growth, and your well-oiled machine is in full effect. This stable operation does not need much input from you as the business owner, and you are financially stable.

Stage 6: Transition

You either start to see business decline or are preparing to merge or sell it. You can look at this as your exit strategy or next step.

Prepare to Shift workbook helps entrepreneurs in the hobby or early startup stages that are committed yet struggling to reach the growth stage. We will review foundational principles that shift your thinking and actions so you can get the breakthrough you need to move through each stage. Each section has application exercises to assess your current business opportunities and uncover helpful next steps relative to that topic. Through this workbook, I offer a foundation that shortens the learning curves involved in business growth and reduces the frustrations associated with taking your business from hobby to thriving company. We simplify the complexity of this process and make it much easier to digest.

Just like the origin of the 37 Oaks' name, a massive oak tree blossoms from a tiny acorn, and that acorn has what it needs on the inside to reach its full potential. Part of my job is to help you see what you have and can do to achieve your vision of operating a profitable, scalable, and sustainable business.

Chapter 2
Set the Tone

Before we dive into this workbook, I want you to take a moment to do two things.

1. Clear Your Mind

This is important because I want you to be in a safe space to absorb new content. Some of this may be new, uncomfortable, or cause questions about how you will do it. So, please start with an open mind to receive the information, and we will discuss the "how" later.

2. Commit to Completion

This workbook is like a puzzle. You can't complete a puzzle with some of the pieces; you must put each piece in its correct space to see the complete picture. So you must read each chapter and complete the exercises as each section builds off of each other. If you skip sections, you may not get the full benefit. We may encourage you to revisit some exercises after you complete the workbook, but we recommend having a good attempt at completing the exercise as you read each principle.

We are proud of you for carving out the time to invest in you and your business. Some of this workbook is a development opportunity for you, whereas others are for your business. So be open to taking inventory of both.

Let's prepare to shift.

Chapter 3
The MindSHIFT

First, we need to prepare for a MindSHIFT. During this stage, your mindset is evolving while learning new skills and gaining hard-earned experiences. It is not one moment in time where the flip switches, and your thinking immediately transforms. You'll find that you have been evolving from the knowledge, setbacks, and experiences throughout your entrepreneurial journey. If you can also understand that your intellect, abilities, and talent can expand, expect to accomplish more than you ever thought possible.

In this section, I want to put the finishing touches on the MindSHIFTS you need to successfully transition your business from a hobby to a growth stage. You have just spent months, or possibly years, in the early startup or hobby stage, so you've learned a lot up to this point, and experiences have shaped your entrepreneurial perspectives. But, we encourage you to be open to absorbing new information and techniques. Many of these principles can make a difference in your progress.

I typically work with underserved, under-resourced, and underfunded small business owners across the United States. Often, they lack access to necessary resources, education, networks, and funds and face disproportionately more challenges than their more privileged peers. I fit into some of these criteria when I began my entrepreneurial journey, so I relate. Therefore, I also understand the importance of being mentally strong and controlled to push a business forward under these circumstances. Our mind is an asset we can activate and mold into a tool to help us succeed despite our background, network, resources, or bank account size. Not only is this necessary for the general journey of entrepreneurship, but it is essential during the critical yet fragile stage of transitioning our business from hobby to growth.

Through this chapter, not only do I want to share what I learned, thought, and practiced as a growing business owner but also the insights gained from coaching over a thousand entrepreneurs over the past few years. This thinking is what I wish I knew before starting my business and, ideally, what I want every entrepreneur to realize and appreciate before they start working with me. Consider what I am about to tell you as "pillars of the mind" for successfully shifting your business into a growth stage.

Successful entrepreneurship has just as much to do with what you think, as it does with what you do. Your actions will be more effective when you begin anything with the right mindset. So, let's first discuss the MindSHIFT needed to unstick your business from the hobby stage and progress towards growth.

1. It's Bigger Than You

"In the journey of entrepreneurship, tenacity of purpose is supreme." – Aliko Dangote.

In transitioning a business from a hobby to the growth stage, one of the first MindSHIFTS I recommend every small business owner to make is to define and grasp the true purpose behind their business' existence.

I have been in the retail, commerce, and CPG industries for over twenty years and have gained much experience and knowledge. I have worked with local and international brands. I have also worked with retailers who own one store as well as larger organizations with over 10,000 locations. I have managed close to $1 billion in corporate revenue and have created products under store brand labels. I've led numerous marketing & assortment planning strategies and have managed retail categories ranging from baby products, hair care, and pet care to incontinence and many in between. My perspective and experience are pretty robust, so you could say that I know a thing or two about the importance of understanding a business' true purpose for existing.

That's why I can say with complete confidence and conviction that entrepreneurs who are clear on the purpose of their business' existence help them understand their value in the market. I call this a "purposeful perspective." This allows you to scale strategically while understanding the impact you can have on a larger market. You also become more aware of your potential and the necessity of achieving it. This is a critical element toward growth and is often underestimated.

Small businesses are not just entities that sell products. They are entities that can deliver an unmet need to an underserved market. This means a customer wants to be serviced in a particular way, with a specific product, and they aren't. They are not getting their needs met in a way that they prefer or need, and small businesses have the ability and structure to change that. You can connect, understand, and build trust with customers through methods that larger companies can't or often overlook. You can innovate, iterate, and move quickly since the red tape of bureaucracy does not stifle you as it does with larger companies. This is one of the most important competitive advantages that small businesses have over larger companies with deeper pockets, larger teams, and more resources. Believe it or not, there are markets you can reach and understand better than your larger counterparts. Getting a purposeful perspective of your business helps you see this.

The extent to which I have seen small businesses impact customers' lives never ceases to amaze me. I have witnessed body balms and shampoos successfully soothe chronic skin issues and help regrow hair for women suffering from medical conditions. I have seen necklaces & earrings help people gain self-confidence and feel sexy in their own skin. I have seen books and affirmation journals guide struggling teenagers through tough high school years. I have witnessed sauces & desserts help those with allergies to feel included, and not an outcast when it comes to traditional and cultural gatherings with family and friends. And I have seen t-shirt lines help the unheard find their voice using clever ways to express themselves.

Body balms, necklaces & journal sets are not new. They exist in the market, and customers have many options. Other businesses likely have products that share many of your product's characteristics. However, the good news is that the value of your product is greater than the actual product itself because what you offer also includes intangible benefits. The combination of product, trust, empathy, service, experience & connection makes you unique. It, therefore, allows you to meet an unmet need from an underserved market in the unique way they need. This is what makes you valuable.

Have you ever heard the saying "Find your why?" This was made famous in 2017 by Simon Sinek in his book *Find Your Why: A Practical Guide for Discovering Purpose.* Sinek believes that achieving fulfillment starts with understanding exactly WHY we do what we do.

Avada.io[1] wrote a blog that included a few examples of WHY statements from companies you may know...

- Spotify is a digital music, podcast, and video service that gives you access to millions of songs and other content from creators all over the world.

---

[1] https://blog.avada.io/resources/what-is-your-why-examples.html

- o *Their Why?:* To unlock the potential of human creativity by giving a million creative artists the opportunity to live off their art and billions of fans the opportunity to enjoy and be inspired by these creators.

- Google is a multinational technology company that focuses on artificial intelligence, search engine technology, online advertising, cloud computing, computer software, quantum computing, e-commerce, and consumer electronics.

  - o *Their Why?* To organize the world's information and make it universally accessible and useful.

Why is it important to understand your *why*? And why are we focusing so much on this topic?

- This is a crucial business exercise and a critical MindSHIFT practice necessary for transitioning your business from a hobby to growth.

- It is one way to define your purposeful perspective. You are doing more than just selling a product. There is a fundamental market need your business is meeting, and the products you sell are just one way you are meeting that need.

- When entrepreneurship gets frustrating and exhausting, you will need a source of motivation. This is a journey with ups and downs, and inevitably, difficult times will arise. We must expect them as well as accept them. When you realize that a group of customers depend on you to do what you do so they can thrive and grow, it is a source of energy and inspiration when times get tough.

- It helps you build a customer-centric business which is a necessary element of success. This means your business strategy and company culture are centered on creating the best experience for the customer. Everything you do and how you do it is about creating value for them.

- It helps define your unique value. More and more are entering the world of entrepreneurship due to the ease of starting a business. Competition is fierce in the marketplace, and customers are bombarded with a multitude of options each day.

According to siteefy.com[2], "Back in 2007, market research firm Yankelovich surveyed 4,110 people and found out that an average person sees up to 5,000 adverts daily. Today, that number is even higher, and the average person sees around 10,000 ads daily, though only a quarter of that or less will be relevant."

If we are not clear in helping consumers understand *why* they should buy from us and no one else, they have no reason to pay us attention, let alone buy from us. Our *why* feeds into what makes us unique. Once this is clear, it needs to be the core message of all our marketing and communication efforts to ensure we break through the noise to get our customer's attention.

---

[2] https://siteefy.com/how-many-ads-do-we-see-a-day/

While in corporate, one of my roles was that of an Innovation Manager that worked on a team researching small business owners. One insight that circulated within our group was that entrepreneurs should all possess some level of ego. For me, the word "ego" always had a negative connotation, so I did not initially agree with the statement. I felt people should be humble because it seems like the right thing to do and because I was taught that it gets you further in life. In growing my own business and working with small businesses across the country, I would now say that the principles of that insight are powerful and correct, but I would make slight adjustments.

Confidence is the word I would use, not ego. Confidence is ego, with a healthy balance of humility. I later learned that both ego AND humility could and should coexist for entrepreneurial success. Each entrepreneur should believe that because of the unique way they can use their business to deliver an unmet need to an underserved market, they are the absolute best person in the world to do what they do. This is confidence.

The reason why you can reach a particular market in a particular way is due to your unique talent. This talent means that you have the innate ability to do something extraordinary without having to exert the same amount of effort as others. Your talent ties into your purpose and is partially expressed through your business. I keep emphasizing that you are doing more than selling products. You have an intangible impact on your customer's life by meeting unfulfilled needs. This is part of WHY your business exists and why people will buy from you and no one else. People depend on you to do what you do because you are the best person to do it. Your uniqueness is unmatched regardless of your background, age, network, gender, race, or bank account size. Therefore, this makes you top tier in impacting and reaching a particular market in only the way you can. It's time to shift our minds to be more purposeful and intentional about scaling our talents to help more people solve their problems and meet their needs. You're delivering something unique and reaching markets other companies haven't and maybe can't.

Understanding your *why* and your purposeful perspective is a process that takes time. But you can see its impact on your business, so it is a necessary process that requires your commitment. As you craft or refine your *why* let me share mine as an example.

My *why* is to help underrepresented, under-resourced, and underserved late-start-up entrepreneurs "unstick" so they can build profitable, sustainable, scalable businesses that impact their families, communities, and global markets. I do this through 37 Oaks Consulting, a commerce development and learning laboratory that educates and prepares entrepreneurs for growth through wholesale, e-commerce, storefronts, and pop-up markets. I am the best person to do this because I have successfully grown my own business under the same circumstances and helped close to a thousand small business owners around the country do the same. My unique mixture of experience, education, interests, skills, and personality allows me to understand my entrepreneurs' challenges and develop a unique toolkit of resources, strategies, and solutions to help them achieve their business goals.

Exercise: It's Bigger Than You

I have said this many times, but your business is more than just selling products. The uniqueness of your experiences, talents, education, network, personality, and interests, allows you to meet a need for an underserved market in only a way you can. They depend on you to do what you do well so they can thrive and grow.

This first exercise is essential and sets the foundation for the remaining MindSHIFT principles needed to successfully transition your business from the hobby to the growth stage.

Use the space below to outline your *why*. This is an iterative process, so as you grow and get more insight on your business, you may want to adjust it, which is fine. Don't worry about getting the final version of your purposeful perspective, but focus on getting a great first draft.

If you have not completed this exercise before, it will certainly be eye-opening. If you have, I encourage you to do it again and be open to revisions if needed. There are various frameworks you can use to craft your why, but you can use the examples below as inspiration. Feel free to elaborate on these examples and use a format similar to mine if you prefer. Make sure you think big and paint a picture that taps into the true essence of *why* your business exists.

- Spotify: To unlock the potential of human creativity by giving a million creative artists the opportunity to live off their art and billions of fans the opportunity to enjoy and be inspired by these creators.

- Google: To organize the world's information and make it universally accessible and useful.

What is your *why*?

_____

_____

_____

_____

_____

_____

_____

_____

_____

_____

_____

_____

2. Growth Is The Only Option

"There is no reason to have a plan B because it distracts from plan A." - **Will Smith**.

In reflecting on 37 Oaks' transition from startup to growth and coaching business owners on the same process, I have seen a shift in intensity, focus, and determination when situations have dire consequences for failure or no alternatives for success. We see this same mentality in our personal lives, too. For example, we know it's wise to adjust our diet to avoid high blood pressure and other health issues, but we still eat that bag of chips or rib tips more often than we should. And for many people, it's only until they experience a health scare, or even worse, a heart attack, that they become serious about consistently eating well.

By October 2014, I had a successful corporate retail career. I was married with a beautiful daughter, and had recently moved to a new city. I had transitioned full-time to the tech startup I co-founded with my husband and our startup was growing, supporting our family, and bursting at the seams with potential. Although my father passed away five years earlier, my mother lived nearby. My husband and I were hopeful about having my mom's support with our daughter, especially as we juggled the dueling demands of entrepreneurship and parenthood.

Then, just 13 months later, I was a divorced, single mom and gradually leaving the startup that had been my sole source of income. Both of my parents had sadly passed away, and the thought of trying to figure out the following steps on my own was utterly overwhelming. Needless to say, a lot can change in a year.

Stressed out was an understatement. I had a small stash of money to support my daughter and I until I figured out other income sources. Each time a bill payment went out and no money was coming in, my anxiety levels soared. In moving to this new city, I had very few (and by few, I mean next to none) professional or personal connections there. Something else had changed within me. After experiencing entrepreneurship, I did not want to return to a corporate career. I now felt empowered and energized from having a taste of business ownership. I knew it could give me a platform to achieve much more than what a larger company could. I just needed the space and autonomy to figure it all out. But, this time, I would have to do it alone as a solopreneur. Besides, even if I wanted to get a company job, that process would take time, and I did not have much to spare!

So what was my plan, I hear you ask? Well, plan A was to quickly figure out what my new business would be AND make it work so that it could support myself and my child. It would give me the flexibility I needed to manage parenthood and tap into this potential I knew was already there. Plan A was my preferred plan, but I only had about 4-5 months to figure things out before all the money I had ran out.

Plan B was to play it safe. In this scenario, I would not pursue entrepreneurship, at least not immediately, and would look for another corporate job. This was not ideal because I needed schedule flexibility, and it would limit my time to work on developing a business that I felt would exercise my potential and talents. I would also put myself at risk of getting "stuck" in corporate...once again.

Plan A had to work. But honestly, Plan A was looking raggedy. I had no business idea or strategy, let alone a sense of when a business could be profitable enough to support my daughter and me. Looking back on it, I took a more significant risk than I realized. Plan B would have been the logical choice, but I decided to dive, head first, into Plan A.

There are two reasons why I believe taking the risk with Plan A generated the results it did. First, I made up my mind that there was no plan B. Plan B was not an option and was not even going to cross my mind as a possible solution. The number of times I said this to myself made me believe I had no other option, even though there may have been other options to consider. This put my mind into a necessary "sink or swim," "fight or flight" mode. If I didn't figure out Plan A, the consequences would be severe. Although life and death were not at stake, it often felt like it was. "If I don't kill it, we won't eat it" was a common statement in my household. I cannot overstate how important this was to my focus, commitment and consistency. This mentality would still hold even if I had it to do all over again with more support and resources. Why? Because it puts me in the strong mindset of "I won't fail."

I believe Plan A generated results because I simply shifted my mental focus from "employee" thinking to a "business owner" approach. I was no longer willing to exchange the potential I knew I could achieve for the security of a consistent paycheck and benefits (no matter how tempting they might be). It was a risk, I have to admit it, but I was ready to take this leap of faith, so that I could tap into the significant impact I knew I could make.

I knew that an uphill battle was on my hands,, and I wasn't naive enough to thinkI would win every battle I would face, but Plan A was going to work. It had to. I was committed to figuring it out, and losing the war was not an option!

Exercise: Growth Is The Only Option

Your business is bigger than you and there is a market depending on you to do what you do so they can grow and thrive. "What happens if I don't fulfill your vision?"

Plan A is your profitable, sustainable and scalable business. Plan B is everything else. What are the consequences if you do not achieve Plan A? What would be the impact on the market you serve and the repercussions on you on a personal level? After you complete the framework below, reflect on the insight revealed, and ask yourself, how does it make you feel and what will be your next steps?

What happens if you don't fulfill your vision?

INTERNAL IMPACTS	EXTERNAL IMPACTS
What are the impacts to self, family, friends & community if you don't fulfill your vision?	What are the impacts to customer & the market if you don't fulfill your vision?
• Won't build & pass on generational wealth. • Won't be the successful entrepreneurial role model that my family & community needs to see. • Won't tap into my full potential. • Need to return to or continue working for others.	• Continue to overpay for underperforming products. • Lack a brand that truly understands their unique needs. • Needs will continue to go unmet and therefore their skin issue will still impact their personal lives.

EXERCISE
What happens if you don't fulfill your vision?

INTERNAL IMPACTS	EXTERNAL IMPACTS
What are the impacts to self, family, friends & community if you don't fulfill your vision?	What are the impacts to customer & the market if you don't fulfill your vision?
• • • • • • • •	• • • • • • • •

3. Your Most Powerful Asset

"Where the mind goes, the man follows" - **Joyce Meyer**.

I wrote this workbook to help "unstick" entrepreneurs who have a deep desire to transition their business from a hobby to growth. There is a clear and fundamental difference between the two stages, and if we understand the distinctions, we can begin to understand the MindSHIFTS required to do this successfully.

A hobby is an activity carried out during leisure time and on a regular basis. At this stage in business, you are casually sharing your talent through your product. There is little to no time to talk about business structures, formalities, financials, or management. You can approach a hobby how and when you want without the pressure of seeing growth. It is perfectly okay to have a hobby or side hustle with no intention to take it beyond what it currently is. You can still be impactful to customers' lives.

Growth is when you have a solid business model and are beginning to strengthen your position in the market. You are making more money, breaking even, and increasing profitability. You have a team (despite the size), a formal and structured business, and are actively working on expansion and scaling up. There is a vision you are working towards, and you are committed to taking on all the aspects of business management to achieve it.

Operational shifts must occur when transitioning your business from the hobby to the growth stage. How you market, produce, and price your product will need to adjust, and how you manage your business, finances, and technology will also need to be tweaked slightly. In addition to what you do, the mental fortitude and control required to make and maintain this transition are often underestimated and overlooked.

We must learn, understand, and respect the power of the mind. What we feed our minds tremendously impacts our journey, success, and growth in entrepreneurship. What you hear and see about your business is at the core of this. Why? Because what you hear and see seeps into your mind and impacts what you think. It starts to form your own perception of your business and your success. What you think impacts what you believe. What you believe impacts what you do. Your thoughts are the foundation of your growth, success, and influence, and your actions are what is needed to achieve your goals.

Think of it as building a house. The mind is like building the frame. It determines the house's height, width, stability, and functions and sets the solid foundation for renovations, developments or expansions. This is why we must pay close attention to how we build the frame of our business, as it determines all things to come.

Hear

Have you heard of affirmations? Affirmations are powerful, positive statements that can help you challenge and overcome self-sabotaging and toxic thoughts. When affirmations are repeated and believed, one begins to make positive changes. How does this happen?

Well, according to healthline.com, *"Your brain sometimes gets a little mixed up on the difference between reality and imagination, which can be surprisingly useful. Creating a mental image of yourself doing something — and saying it out loud- like acing a nerve-wracking interview or conquering your fear of heights by bungee jumping — activates many of the same brain areas that experiencing these situations would."*

What do you think happens when you hear words of doubt coming from yourself or others close to you?

- "I can't do this."

- "This business is never going to work."

- "I am not smart enough to figure this out."

- "You will never be good at selling or public speaking."

- "You don't know what you are doing."

- "Your little business won't grow beyond this city."

What you hear impacts what you think, which shapes what you believe, and influences what you do.

See

After Barack Obama became President of the United States, many people realized that it was now possible for a person of color to be President - a never-seen-before occurrence since the founding of this nation. Perhaps you don't see anyone who has experienced or is experiencing success in entrepreneurship. And what happens when you don't have a strong example of a successful business owner in your community? It can impact how or *if* you see yourself being successful.

Sometimes our environment doesn't provide us with successful entrepreneurs from whom we can watch and learn. Not everyone has the advantage of attending a well-connected university or belonging to a social group with a built-in network they can leverage. Unfortunately, I know and work with many business owners where this is their reality. But this doesn't mean you can't become successful.

This is why finding and connecting with a community of like-minded business owners on a similar path as you are is crucial. If you can't make personal connections, then I highly recommend watching videos and attending events where you can "see" icons in your industry and be inspired, motivated, and directed by them.

Remember what you see impacts what you think, which shapes what you believe, and influences what you do.

When the odds are against us, ingenuity is ignited, causing us to work harder to figure things out. It's OK that you don't have an "it's who you know" privilege to fall back on or a positive environment for motivation. Since we can't always control our circumstances, it is imperative that we are intentional in finding or creating the positive and encouraging narratives we see and hear. How you invest in your growth matters - whether that investment is in you or a like-minded community. However, it may require mental fortitude and a commitment to step outside the lure of the comfort zone.

There is no way my business would have transitioned to a growth stage if I did not quickly learn the power of managing and feeding my mind a steady diet of success stories and positive narratives. It is crucial to nurture and protect your mental strength, focus and that little voice inside your head, even if it means making tough decisions, having uncomfortable conversations, and making changes to people, places, and behaviors that don't align with your goals.

It is too important not to! Your predominant thoughts and consistent actions determine how far you go and how successful you are. Therefore, paying attention to what you regularly see and hear is vital because that can fuel your actions or stall your progress. This is not something you should ever take lightly.

Quitting starts in the mind. But you know what else does? Commitment. Your mind can either produce the power to quit or to commit. And if we don't acknowledge and harness that power and direct it with intention, it will take matters into its own hands, for better or worse.

Exercise: Your Most Powerful Asset

The purpose of this exercise is to take inventory of what you are seeing and hearing about your business. It can come from within yourself or those around you. Complete the framework below and reflect on how this impacts your business's success.

EXERCISE
What are you HEARING & SEEING about your business?

POSITIVE	NEGATIVE	AFFIRMATIONS
What do I hear & see about my business (from myself or others) that is supportive of success?	What do I hear & see about my business (from myself or others) that is NOT supportive of success?	What can I say to myself to combat things I hear that are not supportive of my success ?
•	•	•
•	•	•
•	•	•
•	•	•
•	•	•
•	•	•
•	•	•
•	•	•

4. Purposeful Obstacles

"The more obstacles I overcome, the stronger I become"
- Gracie Alvarez.

As discussed in the "It's *Bigger Than You"* section of this book, entrepreneurship is a journey with many phases, stages, and seasons. There will inevitably be ups and downs; wins and losses; moments when we feel empowered; moments when we feel bound; moments with answers and questions. And sometimes all these moments can take place in one day!

An article in Entrepreneur[3] magazine in 2016 featured a graphic by Derek Halpern (of Social Triggers and Zippy Courses) that does an excellent and accurate job of summing up a day in the life of an entrepreneur. The peaks and direction of this graphic represent the results of our hard work and progress and offers reassurance that we are doing something right. On the other hand, the dips indicate stress, exhaustion, and when we are surrounded by uncertainty and defeat.

A Day In The Life As An Entrepreneur

---

[3] https://www.entrepreneur.com/leadership/what-a-day-in-the-life-of-an-entrepreneur-actually-looks/274831

Unfortunately, this is the harsh reality of entrepreneurship. We may want to reconsider it, if we are not mentally prepared to handle the twists, turns, and emotional roller coasters that come with it all. Great times are welcomed, but challenging times are inevitable, and we must be willing to embrace those too. Transitioning a business from a hobby to growth requires a MindSHIFT that acknowledges & accepts obstacles as valuable, important and strategic. If we don't encounter obstacles, we risk inefficiently scaling our business and covering up the weaknesses in our sustainability plans.

Business obstacles are intentionally designed to strengthen and refine our thinking and strategies so we can reach larger audiences in an efficient, profitable, and sustainable way. In the early-growth stage of operating on a smaller scale, obstacles show us the mistakes we made so we don't make big mistakes when our business expands.

I often say that if we are genuinely doing something innovative, we don't have a blueprint or roadmap to figure it all out because it's never been done before. Therefore, we don't have all the answers in this journey, and acting as we do would be unrealistic and a source of unnecessary anxiety. Naturally, we are going to have moments of questions and moments of certainty. Obstacles typically coincide with moments of question, especially when something catches us off guard or we just don't know which way to turn next.

One way to tackle this is through a MindSHIFT that looks at obstacles as a way to uncover questions and find answers

and control my demeanor so I can lead effectively and make good decisions through turbulent times.

In no way do I want to paint a picture that this is easy. I am just saying that I learned that when you are a leader, you set the tone for your company, and your vibe and demeanor trickle down to your team. Think of when you are flying on a plane. If you feel extreme turbulence and the pilot begins to panic, the passengers and crew will follow suit. The pilot is the leader. If the leader shows control and confidence, those in the cabin will relax and have faith that everything is in hand.

I did not have a team back then, but I am glad that I learned how to manage through turbulent times in the early stages of business ownership vs. learning this lesson when my business was at a larger scale. Now, as I lead a larger team, I've realized that if I didn't gain that experience early on, I could have lost the people who have helped me thrive. I am only as good as my team after all, and obstacles are inevitable. It is too risky to test leadership styles when you already have a team in place. We all know leaders that we would say are not effective; I have put too much into this business not to be effective!

There were also times when I didn't have the funds to run my business. How do you create, market, and grow a business without any money in the bank? We will discuss this in more detail in the WorkSHIFT section later on, but I had to learn to be agile even when it came to finances. And some of this, I had no experience with and, frankly, no interest in learning how to do it. Yet I am thankful to have experienced these challenging moments on a smaller scale because I learned to be resourceful and creative and how to stretch a dollar. I learned how to operate under lean circumstances; prioritize my time and budget, and research affordable options. Although it was a tough learning curve, all these skills are needed (probably more so) in the growth phase and ultimately made me a better entrepreneur.

You gain expertise, insights, and education through obstacles that build a stronger you and a stronger business. You develop resilience, focus, self-discipline, commitment, and perseverance, which are essential for future growth. The value of this should not be underestimated.

As Frankie Beverly said, "Joy and pain are like sunshine and rain." In other words, these phases are inevitable. The pain and the rain (obstacles) are not intended to knock you down but to strengthen you. Learning what to do is just as important as learning what not to do. That's why you see so much confidence in seasoned entrepreneurs. They know how to grow through the chaos. Even though you may not see the benefits of tough times in the season you're in, you must know that they exist and will become more apparent over time.

Exercise: Purposeful Obstacles

The purpose of this exercise is to reflect on obstacles you are currently facing within your business and uncover the ways it is helping to strengthen you and/or your business for future sustainable growth. There is purpose in each obstacle you face during this stage, so let's bring some visibility to it.

EXERCISE

What can I learn from current obstacles that will help my business grow in the future?

CURRENT OBSTACLES Describe the top 3 obstacles I am currently facing in my business.	**WHAT IS THIS TEACHING ME?** What can I learn from these obstacles that will help my business grow stronger in the future?
•	•
•	•
•	•

5. Growth & Comfort

"Growth and comfort do not coexist." **Ginni Rometty, CEO of IBM**

Four years before starting 37 Oaks, I was a co-founder of a technology startup. In the world of startups, when seeking investment from venture capitalists, they prefer businesses to be led by co-founders and teams partially because one person may not typically be proficient in all functions necessary to

39

operate a successful business. People have different strengths and weaknesses, and having multiple people on a team gives you a better opportunity of covering all the bases needed to run a business versus one person trying to do it all on their own.

When it comes to taking your business from hobby to growth, you'll need a combination of mental and operational shifts. And there are about eight functions a business owner needs to manage to achieve this. Although separate, they all must operate in complete harmony to nurture your business.

- Finance
- Product/Services
- Operations
- Marketing
- Sales
- Management
- Human Resources
- Strategy/ Innovation

Try to name a business that has neglected just one of these functions and still experienced remarkable growth and success? Still thinking, right! In the early stages of entrepreneurship, not all business functions may require equal attention, but eventually, all these areas of your business will need to be activated at significant levels.

I have always loved business. When I was a little girl, my best friend and I pretended we were bosses and yelled at "employees" (stuffed animals), fired people, filled out paperwork, and made major company decisions around the dining room table. That was our definition of business at the time. Later in high school and college, I developed a love and understanding of management, financials, economics, marketing, research, and strategy as I learned more.

Fast forward a couple of decades later, when I became a co-founder of a technology startup. My partner led most of the sales, pitches, and presentations. This was his strength, and I was okay with that. Being more introverted meant I could enjoy the background of business. I considered myself the behind-the-scenes-operations person and the silent engine that powered the train. I was comfortable in that position and was very good at it.

Then came my solopreneur launch of 37 Oaks. Now, all business functions fell entirely in my hands. There was no sharing, delegating, or aligning essential business functions with interests or strengths. I could not tap into resources to fill in the gaps in areas I didn't particularly enjoy or considered a weakness. I was now responsible for the entire business's front-end and back-end. Yet that wouldn't be a problem if I could afford to hire someone to help or outsource a function, but that was not the case.

I didn't really like public speaking, sales, and graphic design. I had no interest in it, no interest in learning it, and little experience to fall back on. Despite my feeling, here was the reality of the situation:

- I could **not** exclude these tasks or continue to allocate minimal time to them just because they weren't one of my key strengths and pushed me outside my comfort zone. Initially, I gravitated toward the functions that complimented my strengths and comfort zones: business strategy, marketing, research, finance, and operations. Although I could lay a decent foundation by focusing on my strengths, I knew that to reach the next level; I would have to address my deficiencies.

- I had limited funds, so I couldn't contract positions to cover these tasks and roles. And I wasn't ready to take out a loan to do this as I was still learning how much sales and graphic design contributed to the business. So, I didn't feel I could provide direction or management to a team member.

I knew I could no longer focus on the parts of the business I liked, was good at, and felt most comfortable with. I had to figure out how to fill these gaps without money or support. Public speaking (which included sales pitches and presentations) were tasks I would have been happy to avoid. But, my business was not going to close new accounts, extend its reach or deliver services if I didn't figure this out. So, I committed to being uncomfortable and decided to dive in head-first but start small. I first presented to people I knew, then evolved into smaller groups of people I didn't know. Whether I felt I did well or not, each time I presented, I reflected on what I learned and what could be done differently next time to improve. I then took time to optimize my presentation deck and pitching style. This is what I call "learning sprints."

In learning sprints, we *test* ideas and concepts, *learn* by gathering feedback from the market, *and apply* the learnings to the improved idea or concept. We quickly repeat this process until we finally reach the desired outcome or level of understanding. We don't allocate much time or money to this process until we get further in the sprints and more confident in the returns on investments. Until then, we keep learning sprints on a small scale, so if we make mistakes, it will not be detrimental to the overall business.

Honestly, these learning sprints terrified me, but in signing up to be an entrepreneur, especially a solopreneur, I committed to times of discomfort. I committed to not knowing it all. I committed to facing the unexpected. I committed to overcoming obstacles. I committed to growth. "Growth and comfort do not coexist." My purposeful perspective was at the center of all I do; remember, there was no Plan B. I had to fill this skill gap enough to get me to a space where I could have hired or outsourced someone to do it if that's what I chose.

When I tell people about this part of my journey, they are often surprised because I appear to be a natural when teaching 37 Oaks University courses, conducting interviews, or delivering speeches or presentations. They are impressed with the ease and frequency at which I can present sales pitches or engage in media interviews. I may make it look easy (not intentionally), but this is the result of seven straight years of discomfort and evolution.

Admittedly I still get nervous when I have to do these tasks, and I know I have a lot more to learn, but I have developed the skills necessary to take my business to the next level. As my business grows, I may consider hiring or outsourcing this role as I feel more confident in knowing what would be required, what the results should be, and how to direct, manage and support a team member through these tasks.

Graphic design was another task I would have been *okay* avoiding, but this function was a little different than public speaking. I was good at establishing the design strategy, message, and goals, but translating that into cohesive visuals was not my strength. In the early stages of 37 Oaks, my brand identity was all over the place. There was no consistency or strategy in communications or marketing materials. This included social media posts, email blasts, website design, and sales collateral. Building trust and portraying professionalism and confidence with municipalities, economic development organizations, corporations, and small businesses had to change if I was going to attract and secure the type of clients I needed and desired.

While I didn't have the funds to hire someone to manage these tasks, I could leverage my time once again. I researched free and inexpensive plug-and-play tools for design-challenged individuals like myself. But, even though the tools were great and addressed my design needs, I had an epiphany. It took too long to create cohesive designs, and I certainly wasn't qualified to get this to the level needed! There was a skill required that I could try to obtain but I could never get close enough to in order to deliver to the extent needed. Even though the tools and platforms were amazing, it still required a design eye and skill set that I didn't have to carry that design across all platforms. I was inefficient in this area, which was valuable time I could have spent elsewhere to drive the business forward. So, I could only focus on the minimum needed to get my brand to the next level on my own.

As soon as I had the funds ready to hire a graphic designer, I did. So this experience number one, has helped me prioritize the roles I needed to hire when I had the funds available to do so and two, it helped me understand the definition of the role, expected outcomes, and how to manage, support, and direct team members taking on this part of the business.

You can only focus on what you like or are comfortable doing when it comes to a hobby. With your sights set on growing and reaching larger audiences, you must subscribe to the responsibility of knowing, managing, and leading all eight functions of your business, whether you want to or not. The process of learning new skills and working through weaknesses will be uncomfortable. Learning is the only requirement, not perfection. You won't always know how to do it all, but it must be done when you're the business owner and leader. Being an expert in everything is unrealistic. That's why you'll need to actively spend time in each function of your business to understand its role in your business' growth and get the knowledge to effectively lead, direct and manage a team member through it.

Exercise: Growth & Comfort

In growing a business, we know that everything has to be done, but we don't always know how to do it all. This exercise will help organize and highlight critical business tasks that you either lack the skill or desire to address. It will also highlight their role in your business and provide space to brainstorm ways to address them. I encourage you to review your work with trusted advisors or coaches to get a second perspective.

- **Business Function:** Assign one of the eight core business functions tasks critical to pushing the business forward that you lack the skill set or desire to address. Business functions to choose from: Finance, Product/ Services, Operations, Marketing, Sales, Management, Human Resources, or Strategy/ Innovation.

- **Task or Activity:** List the specific task or activity under the assigned business function that is critical to pushing the business forward. Be specific.

- **Incapable or Dislike:** Write an "I" if you are incapable of completing these tasks/activities because you lack the skills or a "D" you dislike and have no desire to achieve it.

- **Growth Impact:** Assign either a "High", "Medium" or "Low" to describe the importance level of those tasks or activities to the growth of your company.

EXERCISE

Identify the top three critical business activities you are uncomfortable with or lack the skills to implement. See the example below.

BUSINESS FUNCTION	TASK OR ACTIVITY	INCAPABLE (I) OR DISLIKE (D)	GROWTH IMPACT
MARKETING	Marketing efforts that requires me to promote myself, use my likeness or deliver a live video session.	D	HIGH

6. Value In The Process

"Hold the vision. Trust the process" - **Author Unknown**.

One critical exercise we need to complete when transitioning our business from hobby to growth is to take time to document what our business will look like in the future as a thriving and profitable enterprise. This helps us focus on a single goal and provides much-needed direction and guardrails so we can be intentional in our actions moving forward.

To do this, we first have to challenge ourselves to think BIG. Based on our business purpose, write down what the pinnacle of success looks like when we reach it.

Some questions to help you paint this picture are:

Where are all the places your products will be sold?

How many products would you have at this time?

Do you offer both products & services?

What are your annual sales?

How many employees do you have?

Take a moment to write down how this pinnacle of success looks like based on your answers.

The next step prompts you to write down the time you believe it will take to reach this stage. You are not necessarily looking for an exact date, but based on what you outlined, how many months or years will it take for you to get to this point?

Many entrepreneurs I work with ask, "How long will it take for my business to grow?" Although they are asking for a timeline, they are looking for a general timeframe for when they will get answers, clarity, stability, validation, and ultimately relief. They are looking for a sign that their hard work is paying off, reassurance that they are headed in the right direction, and that they will soon get a return on their investment. And I can completely relate and understand this.

Time is a frustrating yet purposeful element of entrepreneurship. We get irritated, impatient, and discouraged when things take "too long," but what does "too long" mean? What factors are we using to calculate "too long"? It is common for small business owners to struggle with "time" during this entrepreneurship journey. But, it is essential to understand and accept that entrepreneurship is a process that takes time. In the short term, we have milestones to reach that will ultimately lead us to the vision. When this frustration arises, we can look at the time it takes to reach the pinnacle of success vs. the time it takes to reach the next milestone towards success. We can learn to recognize, value, and appreciate the time it takes to reach these milestones, or we will get frustrated, discouraged, and paralyzed. A long-term vision may take over 5 years, but we are not in this for just a quick win; we are in this to build a sustainable business.

Although it's not the same satisfaction as reaching the vision, milestones are the critical and valuable efforts that get us towards the vision. Milestones can be broken down into shorter timelines that we can achieve based on our need for motivation and personal preference. They can have targets on achieving this daily, monthly, quarterly, or annual- and anything in between.

Years 1-2: Commit

37 Oaks was founded in January 2016 and the first and second years were very conceptual. If you recall my story, I had no clear definition of what I was doing or what I could do when I started. I knew I wanted to be in the commerce, retail, and distribution fields, and I knew my strengths. Still, I didn't know how to monetize it, who my customer was, the best pricing strategy, the services I was going to offer, or any of the other fundamentals of starting a business. In addition, I could only work on my business about 15% of the time due to other obligations. I quickly learned that the speed, clarity and definition which I sought were tied directly to my capabilities, capacity, and investment.

By the end of year two, I decided to commit by dropping other obligations and focusing full-time on my business. This was a scary space to be in, but necessary due to what I wanted to achieve. This was an essential step because it forced me to commit to investing in taking my hobby or concept into a growing one. So I had to commit to business ownership and everything that came with it. A half commitment was only going to generate half the results. Total commitment does not necessarily mean going full-time, but it was more of a mindshift decision and commitment to invest 100% of what I have to offer so I could see better, faster, and more substantial results. Although this was still part of the early startup stage, this moment was a milestone for me.

Year 3: Build

Year three was all about gaining clarity and definition. Now that I was fully committed to growing the business, my goal was to answer the fundamental questions I could not answer in the "commitment' stage. It is important to note that there was no talk about growth at this time because I didn't know what I was growing. I didn't know who my customer was or should be. I didn't even really know what I was selling. I had more questions than answers, and two more questions arose each time I got an answer.

In working towards clarity and definition, I did a lot of testing and learning. My philosophy was to produce what I believed my customer wanted (test), but the customer confirmed it with their wallet and feedback (learn). I had to be flexible and adaptable because I did not know what might work.

Years 1-3 were rough to say the least. It was laden with much uncertainty, burnout, instability, sacrifice, and risks. But, it all served a purpose in building a foundation for strong and longer-term growth. If you try to skip these challenging stages and the learnings and experiences that come with them, your growth may not be as fruitful and consistent as it could be. It's a bit like building a structure, and these early years are the foundation. How strong will the structure be if you build it on a weak foundation or have missing pieces? If an architect builds a tower on a weak foundation, it will topple before reaching the 3rd floor. If a 6th-grade student skips to high school, all the math and science classes missed in between will make sophomore chemistry more challenging.

I have seen small businesses build these solid foundations and take advantage of unexpected opportunities such as media attention, publicity, or celebrity endorsement because they were prepared for the operational demands of unexpected success. I have seen those who failed to prepare run into many issues along the way. Their e-commerce sites freeze from the influx of orders; the quality of the product is compromised, or they encounter customer service and shipping issues. This turns those first-time shoppers into last-time shoppers. Not having uncovered structural opportunities for improvement in the earlier stages, when the business is smaller, did not prepare them to deliver flawlessly when larger opportunities arose. It is unfortunate to have success knock at your door and not be able to capitalize on it, but if you're not ready it can hinder rather than help your business.

Have you heard of "microwave entrepreneurs" who claim they built their business to six figures within 60 days and can show you how? That sounds attractive, huh? Who doesn't want to be an overnight success? It's easy and quick, and we assume you benefit from profitably selling your product in large quantities without the time and challenges most entrepreneurs encounter. I can't confirm the claims of effectiveness, but I know that if it were tried and true, we would probably see higher success rates in entrepreneurship.

The *Top 6 Reasons Why New Business Fail* article by Investopedia[4] reports, "Data from the Bureau of Labor Statistics shows that approximately 20% of new businesses fail during the first two years of being open, 45% during the first five years, and 65% during the first ten years. Only 25% of new businesses make it to 15 years or more. These statistics haven't changed much over time and have been fairly consistent since the 1990s." They note that one of the reasons businesses fail is due to expanding too fast and not doing so in a strategic way.

Reasons Businesses Fail

Not satisfying a need   Bad business plan   Lack of financing

Bad location   Inflexibility   Rapid expansion

Investopedia

---

[4] https://www.investopedia.com/financial-edge/1010/top-6-reasons-new-businesses-fail.aspx

The goal isn't just growth; it's sustainable growth. This means you can achieve and maintain repeatable and consistent growth without facing major problems. It is tempting to be attracted to alleged promises of microwave entrepreneurship. Still, overnight success does not allow for strategic planning; more importantly, it does not enable you to refine and strengthen the crevices of your business.

Steve Jobs, the former founder and CEO of Apple and arguably the most influential and successful business leader of our time, said, "Overnight success stories take a long time." If you want to grow fast and make quick money, there are probably less stressful and less risky paths than entrepreneurship. There are no shortcuts here. I am not saying opportunities can't quickly catapult your businesses to the next level, but most consumer goods businesses need to undergo a process.

Year 4: Refine

By the fourth year, I was more clear on the direction I was heading with my business. I applied all learnings and improvements and went harder on business development and growth. I felt more confident in what I was selling and to whom I was selling, so my return on investment would be higher than prematurely focused on growth. I still had gaps to fill, but I mapped out my vision and created strategies to reach it. This, to me, was considered a milestone as it was clear I had reached a new and critical stage in achieving my vision.

Years 5-6: Grow

I would consider 37 Oaks' fifth and sixth years as my first years in the growth stage. I confidently and if I say so myself, flawlessly delivered solutions and quickly adapted and adjusted because my business infrastructure was solid. If I had not gone through those tough early years, there is no way I would have been prepared to take advantage of some of the business opportunities that crept up. I grew and diversified my offerings based on customer needs, adjusted my pricing accordingly, and developed credibility in the market with larger accounts.

When the COVID-19 pandemic hit the United States in early 2020, many small business owners and the organizations that supported them were paralyzed. Traditional ways of connecting with customers were disrupted, and we had no idea how long that would last or how to help. Around year 3, I launched a platform under 37 Oaks called SOKONI. It was an e-commerce and retail learning laboratory that helped small businesses get the kinks out of marketing and operations before they scaled into new markets or channels. Online growth was a solution that emerged to support those navigating through the pandemic. Education, resources, tools and support were needed quickly and in abundance. Although imperfect, prior learnings prepared me to take advantage of opportunities from larger organizations that wanted to support small business owners. It helped to propel 37 Oaks further into growth.

Part of the MindSHIFT that needs to happen when you transition your business from hobby to growth is to realize that it takes time to reach your vision. Although skipping steps can be tempting and attractive, this is not a quick, overnight process. This longer-term process's value is getting to know your business and building a structure around it. Building a long-term sustainable business requires time, patience, and commitment. Sometimes the rewards and returns won't be visible until you enter the next phase. Are you okay with that?

I choose to look at my milestones annually. But despite how you look at it, we all must approach entrepreneurship as a marathon. The vision is long-term, and we must pace ourselves and find motivations and ways to preserve our energy. You are building towards a longer-term vision, but milestones are the distance markers that let you know you are firmly headed in the right direction and will make progress. Don't compare your marathon to someone else's. Your journey is *your* journey and completely bespoke to you.

Exercise: Value In The Process

We have learned to trust the process and value the time it takes to complete the process.. Let's revisit two important questions from this section that address both. Use the space below to note your answers.

Describe how the pinnacle of success looks. This vision should be so big that it makes you slightly uncomfortable. Defining your vision has nothing to do with how you will achieve it; it's more about painting the picture. Don't let the "how" stop you from dreaming big. Questions to help you get started are; Where will your products be sold? How many products would you have at this time? Do you offer both products and services? What are your annual sales? How many employees do you have? Are your manufacturing plant, supply chain, and retail stores all owned by you?

_____

_____

_____

_____

_____

_____

_____

_____

_____

_____

_____

Next is to recognize and appreciate the time required to reach your pinnacle of success. Build your vision while setting expectations around the timing to achieve it. How many months or years out will this be? You want to note a general timeframe, so don't stress about exact dates. If it helps, note a time range. Consider your vision, capacity, resources, and capabilities when determining timelines.

---

7. Mind Your Profits

"Running a business well means knowing when it's time to make a profit."- **Auliq Ice**.

When I started 37 Oaks, I didn't know what I was doing, let alone what I should be doing. Even though I had extensive experience and knowledge of the commerce industry, I was launching a new business in a new market. Neither I nor my business had much credibility or reputation in educating and preparing small businesses for growth through commerce. Although retail and commerce fundamentals remained the same for small businesses as in corporate, I was now in a new market. Though I believed I was fully capable and qualified to deliver whatever I set out to do in this field, this was a new audience with little to no prior knowledge, trust, or recognition of my value.

It was a painful and humbling reality when pricing services in the early stages. Pricing is always a challenging topic for small businesses because so many factors go into it. At launch, I chose to discount my prices in order to attract more customers and generate positive testimonials, reviews and valuable case studies to use in marketing. This would help me build credibility with small business owners and the organizations that support them.

My strategic purpose for this particular pricing strategy was to build traction and credibility and show that I could adequately serve this new market. On both occasions, I found myself giving away services. Either I would give in to the "hook-a sista-up" request, or I would come across struggling businesses, and my empathy and emotions would volunteer to help. Reducing prices in exchange for learning, testimonials, and credibility is a strategic approach. Giving away services is not.

Sales and profits took a hit in my early stages, but the experience, learning, and traction were invaluable. I could now answer questions about my target customer, services, pricing, and value. In reaching this point, I knew my pricing strategy was not sustainable, and I could not grow until I took a different approach to my finances.

37 Oaks University is a 37 Oaks platform that teaches classes on costing goods, pricing, and select financial statements. It is interesting to see the epiphanies entrepreneurs have after completing the courses because they realize how much profit they are missing out on and how much profit they need to earn to operate their business. It is common for small business owners to have a similar pricing approach as I had in the early years. We either don't

know how to think about pricing and profitability, sell ourselves short by not making the money we deserve or miss out on learning opportunities.

We have talked a lot about how our business's purpose can be used to help others grow and thrive. Our products or services should not be free or drastically reduced for an extended time. We provide value to the market and should be compensated accordingly. Sure, in the early stages, you may not make as much profit as you would like, but at least you are getting compensated by learning key skills.

Remember, customers are not just paying for the product they buy; they're also paying for all the years of expertise, knowledge, and experience that went into designing and developing the product. Just like product materials and ingredients are essential costs to cover, so are the soft skills that go into making it, namely your expertise.

When you transition your mind from hobby into growth stage, you commit to making profitability more of a focus. You commit to making overall financial decisions that prepare you for upcoming growth. You cannot reach larger audiences if you can't cover expenses, produce more products, market to more customers, hire a team, or generate profits to reinvest in the business. Businesses run off of profits, not sales. Making a sale is nice but is that sale contributing to business growth by bringing in profits? When you make a profit, you have money remaining after a sale to cover your expenses and debts.

In other words, a business can generate many sales, but that doesn't necessarily mean it will make a profit. Sales matter, but we need those sales to be profitable to succeed.

Who wants to get on their business' payroll? Who wants to take a salary? Many business owners I work with transitioning from hobby to growth are not on a payroll, but they want to be. After you can cover your current expenses and debt, the remaining funds can be used to reinvest back into the business or put you on the payroll. Where else does your business get funds to pay you on salary? A profit-centric mindset is a critical MindSHIFT you can make to help you move from a part-time entrepreneur to a full-time business owner. As you envision what success looks like for your business, it should include your salary. Paying yourself may seem like a distant luxury, but growth and stability of your business should come with growth and stability of quality of life.

Exercise: Mind Your Profits

In the early growth stages, profits may not be ideal. It's not until you can optimize pricing and minimize costs that you will see this result. In the meantime, we need to ensure you get "profit" or some value from your transactions. If not financially, at least through learning—list examples of learning objectives that would strengthen your business based on your current business stage. Examples can include building awareness by giving away products or offering significant discounts for testimonials or feedback.

_____

_____

_____

_____

_____

_____

_____

_____

_____

_____

There is nothing wrong with giving away samples, selling at a discount, or donating products. Everything does not have to result in profits. But the reality is that no matter the scale, this impacts your profitability. So, let's establish some boundaries. Describe what limits you can set yourself on providing free and deep discounts?

_____

_____

_____

_____

_____

Chapter 4
The WorkSHIFT

In the MindSHIFT chapter, we discussed seven principles to prepare your thoughts to transition your business from hobby to growth. From here, the foundation of your actions is inspired and ignited. A successful entrepreneurial journey is as much about how and what you think as it is about what you do.

One of my favorite business quotes is by Thomas Edison, "Vision without execution is hallucination." It addresses the two fundamental principles that dictate how and when you reach your vision: strategy and execution.

- **Strategy is the plan.** A filter for decision-making keeps you focused on reaching your pinnacle of success, otherwise known as your vision.

- **Execution is the action.** The measurable steps necessary to implement the plan.

Without a strategy, your execution will be aimless and unproductive. Without execution, your vision is all but a dream. Both are paramount to growth and success. Transitioning your business from hobby to growth requires many actions. So intentional and surgical acts, even if making micro-moves, is crucial to this process.

Remember, what you hear and see impacts what you think, which shapes what you believe, and influences what you do. "Doing" is the ultimate stage of this process. So let's review seven principles needed to transition your business from a hobby to growth.

1. Plan For Execution
"An hour of planning can save you 10 hours of doing"

- Dale Carnegie.

In the MindSHIFT chapter, we challenged you to outline your vision, define goals, and set guardrails for what you will and won't do. Your vision cannot be achieved unless you have a strategy. Your strategy can not be achieved unless you take action. The difference in the growth vs. hobby stage is the need to outline strategies and next steps. It sounds simple but is often overlooked.

Many of the entrepreneurs I work with are creatives. By nature, they are good at dreaming, envisioning, and crafting something out of their imagination. There is no shortage of ideas; they can draw on their creative skills for pulling together an in-the-moment plan or toying around with temporary tactics to help them get from one step to the next. This is often the approach when your business is a hobby, and understandably so. When it's time for growth, entrepreneurs with this personality need to incorporate creativity AND strategy when laying out their growth plans. As you go about this process, consider the following questions.

- What *could* the future of my business look like? (Creativity) And what *should* the future of this business look like (Strategy)?

- How *could* I grow this business? (Creativity) And how *should* I grow this business? (Strategy)

- Where *could* my products be sold? (Creativity) And where *should* it be sold? (Strategy)

- What *could* my product packing look like? (Creativity) And what *should* it look like? (Strategy)

Creativity is a brainstorming exercise to explore all options and opportunities with no guardrails in place. Strategy, on the other hand, is the balance that puts creative thoughts into perspective and scopes out its role in growth by using insights, measurable outcomes, and the realities of the business environment. When developing and implementing a solid plan, creative and strategic thinking should go hand in hand.

After the strategy is outlined, we then have to outline the actions. These are the tasks needed to execute the plan. Speed, flexibility, and focus should be the filter when laying this out.

Speed

In the MindSHIFT chapter, we discussed the importance of assigning a timeline to achieve your vision. The same applies here. For each action to implement your strategy, we should use a deadline to ensure we are moving forward swiftly. Moving fast without compromising quality is critical and can't be underestimated.

Flexibility

Staying firm on our strategies but remaining flexible on how we implement them is a founding principle in this stage. Access to resources, environmental and market changes; industry trends; technology; and competition are unpredictable, so openness to adjust how we operate our business will lead to quicker progress.

Focus

Due to flexibility, change in our actions to implement our strategy is inevitable. Be cautious that this change is not so flexible that it moves you off track from the strategy and guardrails you first put down.

The thoughtfulness around strategy and execution will save time and money and ultimately increase productivity. Do you want to see more from your business and see results quicker? This won't come from wishing for it; we must adjust how we work to see this change.

Exercise: Plan For Execution

Our planning should include both strategic and creative thinking as we move towards growth. It can cause tension in decision-making as these two areas can be in opposition and often conflict. In this exercise, identify one major decision you have made or are making that would benefit from both the creative and strategic thinking approach. It could include decisions related to product packaging, where to sell products or services, marketing plans, hiring for a position, to the type of products you want to introduce.

_____

_____

_____

_____

_____

_____

_____

_____

_____

_____

_____

_____

_____

_____

Next, describe the value of the creative and strategic tension. What would have been the business impact if you only used the strategic or creative approach in making a decision?

_____

_____

_____

_____

_____

_____

2. Customer-centric

"Customer-centricity should be about delivering value for customers that will eventually create value for the company."
- Robert G. Thompson

Have you heard the term "customer-centric"? Business owners are often told to build a customer-centric company, but what does that mean?

A customer-centric company puts its customers at the center of every strategy and creates solutions that fit their needs. This means all strategies, actions, operations, and everything in between put the customer's needs first. On the opposite end of the spectrum is a product-centric company. This places a business' focus on their product, regardless of market demand or customers.

Which philosophy has guided your company so far?

There is no linear path in entrepreneurship. Therefore, the question is not whether your business will operate under a product-centric or customer-centric philosophy, but it's more about when you might use one over the other. Both approaches are valuable and necessary at different points in your business.

An entrepreneur I worked with was closer to the hobby vs. the growth stage and didn't realize they were building a product-centric company until we analyzed their business. It was not a deliberate decision of theirs but rather a result of how they first started their business. In this early stage, they didn't have enough data and market feedback to determine who their customer was, so they couldn't design their business around them. So initially and naturally, their approach would be more product vs. customer-centric.

Focusing on the product is more manageable when trying to gain clarity and direction early in the process because it is tangible, more controllable, and easier to understand - especially since you are still learning about your customer and market. Most of us don't even realize that we have made this decision, so how would we know that we need to make a deliberate decision to adjust our thinking when evolving our business from a hobby to growth? The product-centric stage is still valuable and can be used strategically. Use it to collect data and insights and learn your customer's responses to your product, strengthening the customer-centric approach.

Ultimately, to shift our business from hobby to growth, we must be willing to commit to the customer and make business decisions based on their needs and experience. When your customer's needs shift due to market changes, technology, or environmental issues, would you consider adjusting your product to accommodate the customer's new needs? Or are you so locked in on the product that you refuse to deviate from what you have already delivered to the market?

The bigger question is: Are you committed to the product you want to provide or to the customer you want to serve?

It is never too late to put the customer's needs first and evolve into a customer-centric model. Your products and operations can all be developed around the customer as you strive to create a positive experience at each and every touchpoint. There are benefits to this. For one, it helps attract and retain more customers. Satisfied customers are more likely to continue to do business with you in the future and make recommendations. Plus, a customer-centric approach helps distinguish your business from competitors offering similar products and services.

In 2020, no one anticipated how significantly the COVID-19 pandemic would affect small businesses. Across the country, small business owners were hit hard. Most entrepreneurs I worked with were in the physical retail sector, whether they operated storefronts, retail shops, or pop-up markets. During this time, they started to experience a lot of confusion, stress, and uncertainty, especially when lockdown mandates prevented their customers from leaving home to shop in-store. There was no more "business as usual."

Although 37 Oaks works with small business owners, they are not necessarily the actual purchasers of our services. Municipalities, corporations, organizations, and financial institutions can sponsor our programs to support small business owners in their communities. Small business owners can be the users of our services, but they are not the purchasers. However, small business owners' needs remain at the center of our work.

In all honesty, my team and I did not know how to make it through the turbulent and unprecedented times brought on by the global pandemic. Due to our expertise and experience, our approach was that we would figure it out. But many of the entrepreneurs we worked with didn't have this to fall back on or tap into. Our suite of services at that time could partially support them, but they needed more. They needed something we didn't have. So the question was, did it make sense to deliver these new needs based on the infrastructure and scope of our business, and are we willing to invest in doing so?

During these disruptive times, small businesses needed resources, education, and preparation to duck the punches of entrepreneurship. We tapped into our resources, experts, experience, coaches, and backgrounds and developed and launched the 37 Oaks University Bob & Weave Series for free! This was a series of interviews and live Q&As with industry experts and successful business owners on crucial topics they needed to understand. Marketing, sales, strategy, e-commerce, wholesale, and market research. You name it. It was indeed a labor of love for the people we served. We called in favors and volunteered our time and funds to coordinate, market, and deliver this breakthrough series.

I didn't know just how much the pandemic would impact 37 Oaks.

But I was confident that we would figure it out. It was not the first time we encountered challenges, so our business was built on flexibility. I was fully aware and convinced of my WHY, which is to help underrepresented, under-resourced, and underserved late-start-up entrepreneurs "unstick" so they can build profitable, sustainable, scalable businesses that impact their families, communities, and global markets. No matter what happens, that customer-centric, purposeful perspective remains.

Unbeknownst to me, the customer-centric approach that led to the Bob & Weave Series would have a massive impact on my business. As a result of creating this series, we built trust with small businesses across the country. These connections helped uncover new customer insights, launch new products and services, and inspired new business models we could offer small business owners post-pandemic. We also positioned ourselves to municipal, corporate and organizational partners as a company with an extensive toolbox of turn-key solutions, resources, and education for growing product-based businesses. Our focus on our customers catapulted 37 Oaks deeper into growth when we probably had the most uncertainty in the business' existence.

Customer-centricity means committing to the customer and having a level of responsibility for meeting their needs if it fits within your business direction and scope- even if, at that moment, there is not a clear advantage to you. It is putting customers at the center of all that you do.

Exercise: Customer-centric

Designing your business around a product-centric and customer-centric approach may be necessary at different times of your business life cycle. Again, the distinct nature of each method may cause tension in decision-making, but this tension has value. Answer the questions below to determine whether you have a customer-centric approach or you need to refocus and develop one.

Give examples (if applicable) of when your business may have led under the **product-centric** approach.

_____

_____

_____

_____

_____

_____

Give examples (if applicable) of when your business may have led under the **customer-centric** approach.

_____

_____

_____

_____

_____

_____

Identify **two additional ways** you can emphasize the customer-centric approach of your business.

_____

_____

_____

_____

_____

_____

3. Test, Learn & Apply

"Giant leaps are just a bunch of baby steps strung together"
- Author Unknown.

Years ago, I read *The Lean Startup* book by Eric Ries, which changed how I looked at innovation, business, and entrepreneurship. This book analyzes the process of helping entrepreneurs determine whether a given product or business idea would be viable and profitable by testing assumptions. The goal is not to obtain a golden answer. Instead, reaching a point of increased confidence and comfort in making business decisions can generate a greater return. A framework I often use with small business owners transitioning from hobby to growth is based on what I've learned from this book's principles. I call it "Test, Learn & Apply." This framework provides insight on where to invest your time, money and efforts to build a profitable, sustainable & scalable business. Let's discuss this framework.

Test

We don't have all the answers. We can't. There is no roadmap or template when we are truly doing something unique. We have to be ok with making strategic and well-thought-out assumptions and putting them into the market where it is not as perfect as we would like. Progress is a priority over perfection. It's not perfect, but we are meeting the basic customer needs while collecting customer data.

Minimum viable product (MVP) is a term that was coined and defined in 2001 by Frank Robinson and then popularized by Steve Blank[5] and Eric Ries[6] (author of *Lean Startup).* It does not require perfection before release; in fact, it shies away

---

[5] https://en.wikipedia.org/wiki/Steve_Blank
[6] https://en.wikipedia.org/wiki/Eric_Ries

from it. The MVP has just enough features to be usable by early customers, who can provide feedback for future product development. Results from the MVP lead to incremental improvements in these products.

This testing stage uses our findings to determine whether investing in our initial concept, hypothesis, or assumption is high-risk or low-risk.

Learn

In the test phase, what did you learn about your concept, hypothesis, or assumption? Whether the results are what you want to hear or not;

What are customers saying?

What data have you collected?

What do you need to adjust to serve the customers better?

Does it support or refute your assumptions or hypothesis when you analyze the data collected?

Are there any learnings or trends in the data you can use to learn more about your customers, market, and product?

In this stage, we must be intentional about learning and collecting data that improves our products and services. We don't just want to test for the sake of it.

Apply

Collecting data and insights from the learning stage are essential, but now, what will you do with the information gathered? You learned something new, so now what? We don't have time, resources, or waste in the test and learning phases, so make sure you do something with them. How can you improve products and services based on market feedback? These new insights are designed to enhance the original concepts, assumptions, and hypotheses so you can put them back in the market to collect more data and insight once again.

When you go through this process, you become more comfortable and confident in your offering and how to reduce the risk of investing further by taking your concepts to the next level. A vital consideration of the Test, Learn, & Apply framework is that this process needs to be implemented quickly and inexpensively. You should spend enough time and money to gather the minimum amount of data necessary to collect impactful insights. It's not about perfection, and it's not about a full-blown concept launch; it's about leveraging the customer and market to help you grow strategically.

Entrepreneurs often put too much pressure on themselves to know all the answers or have the correct ones. I do understand why. Sometimes it's because we're so eager to see results; sometimes, we eagerly need results. My experience has taught me that no matter how much we plan, we can't predict where our business will go and when our business will get there. We can't plan to have all the answers. We can influence certain outcomes, but we cannot control them all. Ultimately, the customer tells us what they want when they communicate it with their wallet. They tell us if our plan is working. This is why it's critical to be confident in the customer you want to serve and continually listen to what they have to say.

Exercise: Test, Learn & Apply

In prior sections, we discussed having a long-term vision and using milestones as markers to indicate that you are headed in the right direction and progressing towards that vision. We also discussed flexibility in how you reach your vision, as your plans will inevitably change. This exercise uses the test, learn & apply framework to help you achieve milestones.

List a recent idea you are interested in testing out or introducing.

_____

_____

_____

_____

_____

_____

_____

_____

_____

What does the M.V.P (minimum viable product) of this
concept look like?

_____

_____

_____

_____

_____

_____

_____

_____

List three specific things you would want to test during
the M.V.P. stage.

_____

_____

_____

_____

_____

_____

_____

_____

_____

_____

_____

_____

4. Optimize Assets

"Great opportunities come to those that make the most of small ones" - **Author Unknown**.

Entrepreneurship requires time, sacrifice, energy, resources, and funds. This can make things particularly challenging for business owners that are under-resourced, underfunded, and underrepresented. The help and support they need to overcome common challenges are not readily accessible, such as business education, influential networks, capital, and mentorship. Although their business ideas are innovative and packed with potential, they will face unique challenges on their road to growth.

I observed that we often don't comprehend the number of resources or assets we have at our disposal. Sometimes, we don't see or haven't yet explored, researched, or optimized them enough to know that they exist. It is easy to get frustrated because we don't have what we feel we need to grow our business, or we don't have what we see that others have. But to transition our business from a hobby to growth, one WorkSHIFT we need to make is around optimizing the resources and assets we DO have, as that may be sufficient enough to take us through to the next level.

What DO I have? This is a question I challenge you to answer. Take inventory of what you have in your toolbox. Often, the assets we have to help move our business from hobby to growth tend to fall into one of 3 categories: funds, support systems, and time.

Your Funds

Access to funds (capital + money) enables you to hire or outsource a team and buy necessary tech, software, and hardware to help your business grow.

Your Support System

We may not know the CEO of the largest retailers in the world, have an influential alum network, or have access to the best global sourcing contacts, but look closely at the network you do have. What skills, connections, or resources do people around you have that can enhance your business? Where have they worked? What are their knowledge bases? Who is in *their* network that can support you?

Your Time

Through my experience, although it may be limited, many small business owners I work with tend to have more time to invest in business growth than funds or support systems. If you have funds, you may be able to purchase software, technology, apps, tools, and business coaches needed to help you grow. But if you don't have funds, you can learn and leverage many free and low-cost solutions available. However, it requires time to research and use.

If we don't have funds, we have to allocate our own time or solicit support from others. If we don't have the time to invest, we need funds or support from others. If we don't have support from others, then we need our time to invest or funds to move the business towards growth. Whichever we do have, we have to optimize it enough to generate what we don't have.

I had little money early on in my entrepreneurial journey, and my support system for launching and building a business was minimal. The main asset I had, although not a lot, was time. I had to invest my time into researching and doing the things I could not afford to hire someone to do it for me. I had to use my time and learn the skills required to become my own website designer, graphic designer, and sales team. I had to optimize what I had at my fingertips to generate traction and funds to get what I didn't have. I used free graphic design tools to generate profitable sales so I could eventually hire a graphic designer. I used inexpensive accounting software to track and manage finances to profitability so I could eventually afford an accountant. To grow your business, you'll need to optimize less-than-ideal yet effective solutions to grow. I still needed to invest my time in discovering free or affordable resources, courses, and tools to learn how to do what I needed to get to the next level. Although I didn't have much time for all of this, I had more time than I did funds or a support system.

Optimization is when we get the most out of everything we DO have. It may not seem like we have enough or may not have it to the standards we feel we need, but we will make it enough to get us to the next milestone. Don't leave a drop of benefit behind or let anything go to waste. Are you tapping into all that you have and what it offers? Are you leveraging the current education, coaching, mentors, platforms, tools, and networks you have access to? Focus on what you DO have.

Exercise: Optimize Assets

This exercise identifies current resources you have underestimated or missed that can be used to grow your business. We are going to build off of the work you started in the Growth = Discomfort exercise in the MindSHIFT chapter. Here you listed the tactics and activities you disliked or were incapable of doing but were critical to your success. Now, we need to address how you will address these gaps by either using your time, your funds or your support system.

EXERCISE

Based on the HIGH & MEDIUM growth impact tasks & activities identified in the Growth & Comfort section, place an"X" by the approach you will use to address that gap. See example below.

TASK OR ACTIVITY	YOUR TIME	YOUR FUNDS	YOUR SUPPORT SYSTEM
Marketing efforts that requires me to promote myself, use my likeness or deliver a live video session.	X		

5. Find Your Tribe

"You are the average of the five people you spend the most time with," - **Jim Rohn**.

Entrepreneurship can be a lonely journey, and those around us may not understand how this path can take a toll on your mind, body, and spirit. Many small business owners I work with do not have access to mentorship or networks of people who have experience turning ideas into large, sustainable businesses. Hiring team members, business coaches, or accountability coaches can also be challenging without funds or a network. This makes it challenging for entrepreneurs to surround themselves with the human support needed to navigate this journey successfully.

Those closest to you have the most influence over what you see and hear about your business, impacting how and how fast you grow. In evolving your business from hobby to growth, one WorkSHIFT that needs to occur is the intentionality of who is in our realm of influence. We need strategy, operation, and emotional support, so our close influencers need to fall into one of these four categories.

Strategic Advisors & Mentors

Even if you are not ready to have a formal board of directors, establishing a "circle of advisors" is a way to structure a group of mentors, coaches, and sponsors to help direct your vision, strategy, execution, and growth. They tend to have extensive experience in your field and in the areas you need the most support. Their network is robust, but their wisdom and knowledge are what you need most.

Connectors & Brand Advocates

This group is considered brand ambassadors and advocates because they understand your business' purpose and subscribe to the mission. They heavily influence your ability to grow & scale because they connect you to resources and customers that may otherwise be difficult to find.

Suppliers

Your success is heavily impacted by the network and caliber of your suppliers. A lack of timely, responsive, reliable, and affordable service from your supplier has a trickle-down effect on the rest of your business. If they are not delivering stellar results, then more than likely, you won't be either. Doing your due diligence and vetting suppliers will pay dividends in the long run.

Peers

Connecting with like-minded entrepreneurs can provide the most needed real-time operational and emotional support. As mentioned, this can be a lonely and taxing journey, so you need the help of those who can intimately relate to where you are. Not only is it helpful to have those that are in a similar business stage as you, but also have those that are further along in their entrepreneurial process. They can coach you on navigating the challenges they have had to overcome. Lastly, you want to have business owners you can mentor in your network. Supporting others helps you realize how much you have grown while contributing to building the community you needed when you first started.

You may not have someone to fit each category right now, but to successfully shift your business from hobby to growth, you'll want to work towards this. At this time, the nature of these relationships can be as formal or casual as you'd like. The most important thing is that the relationship is established and cultivated. As you are building your tribe, consider these points.

- We understand the influence of those with a front-row seat on what you hear and say about your business. We would be remiss if we did not mention the opposite side of this spectrum. Having the right people in these spaces is essential, but there may be times when the wrong people are in these spaces. Remember your purposeful perspective? That is too important not to protect. You may have circumstances where you may need to have tough conversations or make tough decisions with shifting people that are not positively impacting your growth and development.

- In each of the four groups we discussed, your goal is to get the people that will add the most value to growing your business. As you consider who can fill these roles, some may be filled by people you currently know, and the rest may be filled by people you have yet to meet. Some may be in your network, others in places you have not yet been. To fill these roles, you have a wide net to cast and a global environment as a source. You are not limited by your location or by the people you already know. Diversification applies not only to reducing business and operational risk but also to learning sources. Learning from people with different perspectives, backgrounds, ages, locations, and experiences will pay dividends in the long run. Be open and excited to expand your network to those you don't usually get to engage with.

Exercise: Find Your Tribe

This exercise outlines the current state of the strategy, operations, and emotional influencers essential to successful growth. Complete the following grid and identify areas of strength and areas that need strengthening. What did you find?

Complete the following grid and identify influencer categories of strength and areas that need strengthening.

Influencer Category	List Name of Current Influencers	What Value Do They Bring To The Company?	Are You Leveraging & Optimizing This Relationship to the Fullest Extent?
STRATEGIC ADVISORS & MENTORS			
CONNECTORS & BRAND ADVOCATES			
SUPPLIERS			
PEERS			

6. Diversify

"Strength lies in differences, not in similarities"
- Stephen R. Covey.

As you transition from hobby to growth, you will create new products and services and enter markets beyond your existing ones. This is called diversification. Growing through this strategy can boost an already successful business or jumpstart one that's struggling.

Why do you need to build your business with diversification in mind? It is an excellent way to generate more sales from customers and decrease growth risks, whilst increasing business sustainability. The market, customers, technology, competition, and the economy will change throughout your entrepreneurial journey. Remember when the COVID-19 pandemic impacted the world in spring 2020? Customers were accustomed to buying products in physical stores, but lockdown and "shelter in place" orders were mandated, and in-store shopping was no longer an option. They now had to purchase many products online. The full extent and impact of the pandemic were unforeseen and unexpected. Some small businesses had operational and functional e-commerce sites, but many did not. Many had to close down because they were too reliant on a traditional brick-and-mortar sales model, which put them at a higher risk when the market changed.

37 Oaks University courses are a popular product within the 37 Oaks brand. We have over 30 courses that build entrepreneurs' retail, commerce, and distribution knowledge. In launching this platform, I first focused on developing wholesale courses. With decades of experience as a national buyer for some of the largest retail organizations in the United States, wholesale was an area I knew like the back of my hand. I had the network and first-hand experience to create and deliver these courses.

After launching, I realized that only offering wholesale courses was probably too risky. For nearly 20 years, I was trained to keep my finger on the pulse of the retail industry, and I knew it had ups and downs, as all industries do. I knew there were times when wholesale was an attractive distribution channel and when it was not. I also knew this was not the only channel that small businesses were interested in selling their product through. What would happen to 37 Oaks if the wholesale market declined? How much of the market was I missing out on if I only focused on wholesale?

With my purposeful perspective and vision in mind, I had to think about ways to provide more of what my customers needed. Here's where the course expansion to e-commerce, storefronts, pop-up markets, strategy, and operations series originated. Diversifying my core offering was not only a growth strategy but also a risk mitigation strategy. I wanted to offer education in different yet complementary distribution channels so my business would not be vulnerable when, not if, the market changed. Before the COVID-19 pandemic, 37 Oaks University's popular curriculums were the wholesale and storefront series. After the pandemic, wholesale and storefront interest dived, and e-commerce courses and programs took off. If we had not diversified, our business might have been forced to close and our only revenue stream would have dried up.

Exercise: Diversify

This exercise focuses on thinking through what diversification looks like for your business. However you diversify, you want to ensure it relates to and leverages the core of your business.

If you are a candle company, you may think twice about diversifying into organic baby food. However, aromatherapy diffusers, DIY candle-making classes, or selling your products in other countries may be more aligned. If you are an all-natural pet food company, you may find moving into women's jewelry a bad decision, yet, pet clothes, accessories, or even pet health care services may be a good fit.

Consider your current business and use the following matrix to list what diversification could look like for you. Here are some prompts to get your brain going.

- Sell the same or slightly adjusted product in different geographies.

- Create new yet complementary categories of products and services.

- Sell into new distribution channels (wholesale, e-commerce, storefront, or pop-up markets).

- Sell to new or expanded customer profiles.

What could diversification look like for this pet grooming company?

DIVERSIFICATION MATRIX	CURRENT CUSTOMER	NEW CUSTOMER
EXISTING PRODUCT	• Travel and trial size version of existing product.	• Expand current products to European market.
NEW PRODUCT	• Expand into pet treats category..	• Not ready for this level of diversification just yet.

EXERCISE
What could diversification look like for your business?

DIVERSIFICATION MATRIX	CURRENT CUSTOMER	NEW CUSTOMER
EXISTING PRODUCT	• • • •	
NEW PRODUCT	• • • •	

7. Promote Wins & Milestones

"Accept that if you don't do shameless promotion, you'll end up with nameless promotion!" - Debbie Allen

People like to associate with winners, and customers, vendors, employees, investors, and partners are no different. In the hobby stage, building solid relationships with each of these groups may not be on your radar as these roles might not always play a part in your overall business success. But, as you shift to the growth stage, they are necessary to build a profitable, sustainable, and scalable business.

Publically celebrating and showcasing your wins helps to feed the narrative of the successful business you are becoming. Seeing a consistent progression of wins builds potential stakeholders' confidence and trust in you; which in turn helps validate your value, and helps to give context to your business plan, and enables you to stand out from the competition. Consider this as a business marketing technique. Initially, they may not know much about you, but through these promotions and communications, they begin to learn and understand you, which is a significant step toward building future partnerships and engagements.

Any activity that represents growth and achievement should be announced and shared with these stakeholders, no matter how big or small you think they are. This can range from customer testimonials, media mentions, awards, acknowledgments, events, new products, closing a significant account, entering a new market, or testing a new business model. It shows your progress towards success, which is attractive to this audience.

Merriam- Webster defines self-promotion as "the act of furthering one's own growth, advancement, or prosperity: the promotion[7] of oneself." It is always interesting to see how many entrepreneurs are uncomfortable with self-promotion as they see it as a form of bragging or a display of arrogance vs. a necessary activity in business ownership, especially for ones in the growth stage.

In December 2019, Debbie Allen wrote an article in *Entrepreneur* magazine called *Using 'Shameless' Self-Promotion to Grow Your Business*[8]. *She* noted one quote that sums up this topic well, "Accept that if you don't do shameless promotion, you'll end up with nameless promotion." And I tend to explain this during my classes. People can't buy from you if they don't know you exist. We are not just talking about marketing your business; we are talking about marketing strategy. Typically, people don't buy or engage with us after seeing your company name for the first time. We need to invest in the process of earning their trust, and promoting each win and milestone is just one of the many effective ways of doing this. Mild promotions and communications may have

---

[7] https://www.merriam-webster.com/dictionary/promotion

[8] https://www.entrepreneur.com/growing-a-business/using-shameless-self-promotion-to-grow-your-business/343139

been in your purview in the hobby stage, but it is a necessary and intentional WorkSHIFT that needs to happen as you work towards growth.

Once I had a vision for 37 Oaks, I locked in on what I wanted my business to be when it grew up, and it certainly wasn't small. I envisioned which geographies it would serve, company culture, diverse business models, team size, revenues, product and service offerings, and so much more. Even though I was seeking clarity and direction on how to get there, I promoted business wins and milestones as though 37 Oaks was a well-oiled, mature machine. In my mind, it was, but my money, time, and support systems didn't reflect this at the time, but like always, I was going to figure that part out. That had no impact on the capability of being a big business; these were just short-term obstacles I had to overcome. Those details would not stop how I or others saw my company's potential.

Looking back on email blasts, flyers, and social media posts, although designs and branding had opportunities, it was clear that the focus was to showcase the hard work and let people know this was not a game. From launching my first course, getting my first account outside of Chicago, having my first team meeting, offering my first class in Spanish, to landing my first national partnership, these wins were all promoted. Was I figuring out many of the details behind each of these as I announced it? Absolutely. But the point was that my hard work led to these accomplishments, and the stakeholders I would eventually need to buy, or partner with me would be able to see this progress, whether I knew it or not. The posts and marketing activity built awareness, credibility, trust, validation, and an understanding of my value. I can say with complete confidence that constantly promoting wins over the years, many of the accounts, partners, and customers I gained early on.

Exercise: Promote Wins & Milestones

How can you be intentional about promoting wins and growth?

_____

_____

_____

_____

_____

_____

_____

_____

Chapter 5
Call To Action

You just completed a workbook outlining proven principles to shift your hobby to a growing business. Congratulations! This is the first step in shifting. How do you feel? If anything, I hope you feel enlightened, empowered, excited, and incredibly motivated. You now have the tools to begin seeing a transformation in your business.

Let's recap the key principles outlined in this book:

The MindSHIFT: how we must think to shift our business from hobby to growth.

1. **It's Bigger Than You:** Grasping your company's purposeful perspective helps you become more aware of your potential and the necessity of achieving it.
2. **Growth Is The Only Option**: Success is the only option. There is no Plan B.
3. **Your Most Powerful Asset:** Protect and manage what you feed your mind. Remember, what you see and hear impacts what you think, which shapes what you believe, and influences what you do.
4. **Purposeful Obstacles:** There is value in obstacles. Embrace and expect them. They uncover questions,

which help you to find answers and reduce risks for future growth.

5. **Growth & Comfort:** Prepare to be uncomfortable with learning and doing things that you are not good at or dislike.

6. **Value In The Process:** Trust the process. Understand and accept that entrepreneurship is a process that takes time.

7. **Mind Your Profits:** Businesses run off profits, not sales. You cannot reach larger audiences if you can't cover your expenses, produce more products, market to more customers, hire a team, or generate profits to reinvest in your business.

The WorkSHIFT: what we must do to shift our business from hobby to growth.

1. **Plan For Execution:** Have a formal strategy. It will save time and money and increase productivity.

2. **Customer-centric:** Put your customers at the center of all you do. Commit to your customers and be responsible for meeting their needs.

3. **Test, Learn & Apply:** Use this framework to reach the point of confidence in making business decisions that generate a greater return.

4. **Optimize Assets:** Optimize the resources and assets you DO have, as that may be sufficient enough to take you through to the next level.

5. **Find Your Tribe:** Make intentional decisions on who you allow into your realm of influence. They have the most influence over what you see and hear about your business, impacting how and how fast you grow.

6. **Diversify:** Mitigate risks as you grow by creating new products and entering markets beyond your existing ones.

7. **Promote Wins & Milestones:** Publicly celebrating and showcasing wins helps potential stakeholders learn and understand you, which is a significant step toward building future partnerships & engagements.

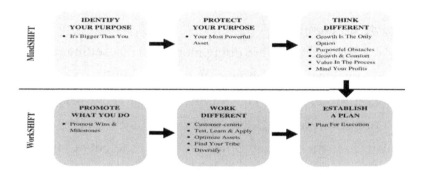

What's next? Each principle has an exercise that helps uncover gaps and opportunities within your business. Now is the time to go back and review each exercise and begin addressing those gaps and opportunities while applying these 14 principles to your business.

This process may take time to get through, and you might see some changes quicker than others, but it is important to stay committed and consistent to see all changes in your business. If you do this, you should see progress within the next 4-6 months. At that time, we recommend re-reading this workbook and redoing the exercises to see how much you have grown. You have decided to take your business to the next level, but are you willing to commit to what it takes to get there? If you want to see a genuine transformation, then you must shake things up and do something different. This phase of entrepreneurship starts with applying seven principles of *thinking* differently and ends with the seven principles of *doing* differently.

Remember, you are doing more than just selling products. Your business has a bigger purpose behind it. You have a market of customers just waiting for you to do what you do so they can grow and thrive too. They are counting on your business to meet an unmet need and service them in a way only you can. You have a responsibility to yourself and to them to grow and succeed. You now have the tools to get started, so let's go! Go fast and go far.

Made in the USA
Middletown, DE
14 October 2022

12686254R00060